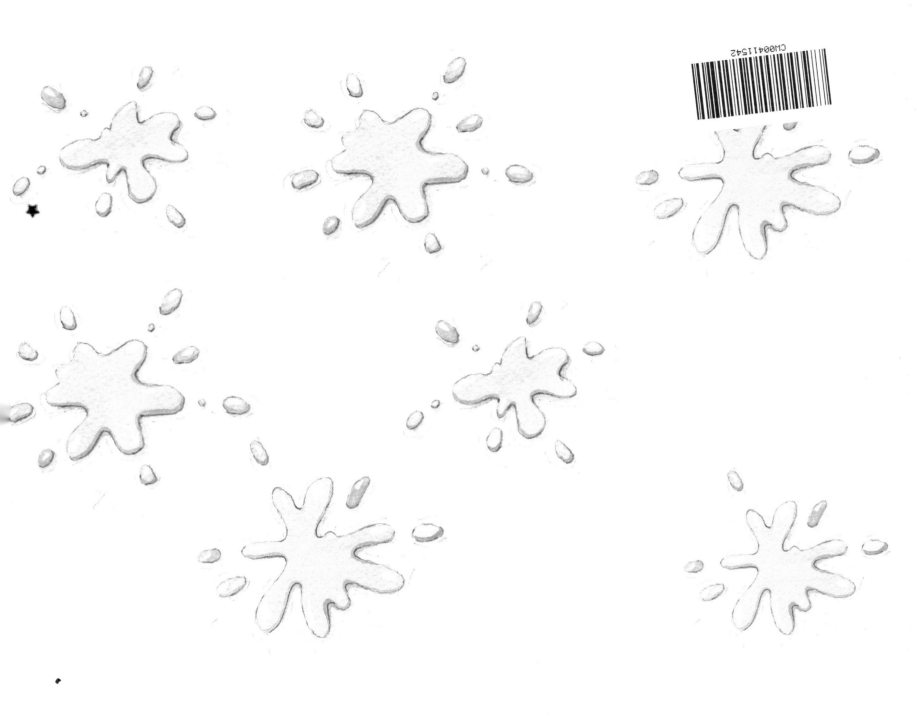

...ling on Custard

Written by Jo Burke

Illustrated by Phillip Price

To Sam

Enjoy!

For Noah
An inspirational little treasure
@hugsfornoah

First published in the UK 2016 by EZE Publications.

ISBN 978-0-9576250-1-3

Age 3+

Contents

Standing on Custard

I like to stand on custard.
I love the way it feels.
My toes are oh so sticky,
The colour of daffodils.

Did you know that you can actually stand on custard?
You can - it's true!

Best Friend

My dog and I, we are best friends.
He even comes to school.
He sits in class and wags his tail.
He's really rather cool.

Asparagus Pickle

Asparagus Pickle was only little,
She loved to laugh and tease.
She picked her nose and stone the crows,
Said "I think this is best served with cheese".

Heaven

If doggies go to heaven
Cats are up there too.
Heaven must be crowded
Much more like a zoo.

Wasn't Me

Just because I did it.
I always get the blame.
How do they all know it's me?
It's really such a shame.

Quiet as...

Worms worm,
Snakes snake,
Horses horse around.
Squirrels squirrel away their nuts in May.
While a mouse... it doesn't make a sound.

Christmas Turkey

"Why did the turkey cross the road?"
Said a cat sat on the kerb.
The dog next door said
"I'm not sure - it's really quite absurd".
Said Mr Toad "Don't you know?
It's Christmas Eve today.
Turkey's on the menu - he's decided not to stay".

99 Please

Ice cream van!
Ice cream van!
Come to my street as fast as you can.
The sun is out, the sky is blue.
I'm very dry, my throat needs you!

Jelly Dog

I would like a jelly dog.
He can be a smelly dog.
A doggy wearing wellies dog.
That's the dog for me.

Busy Bee

Monday I go dancing, standing on my toes.
Tuesday I go swimming, water up my nose.
Wednesday I ride horses, trotting to and fro.
Thursday I do baking, cakes upon the stove.
Friday I play football, saving lots of goals.
Saturday and Sunday really are a treat.
Monday to Friday I'm rushed right off my feet.

Fat Cat

There once was a cat called Frumpy.
Who ate so much he got dumpy.
He ate and he ate,
'Til it was too late.
So Frumpy is now rather lumpy!

Fishing

Ooops I've caught a cold.
A very fine catch indeed.
I caught it with a rod,
On the river by the reeds.
It started with a sneeze, so I reeled it in.
Then it coughed and wheezed,
So I threw it back again.

Barnaby Flea

I have a little friend,
That no one else can see.
His name is Bouncing Barnaby,
And he's a circus flea.
Barnaby is fearless.
He's smashing on trapeze.
Dashing on the tightrope,
While balancing on peas.

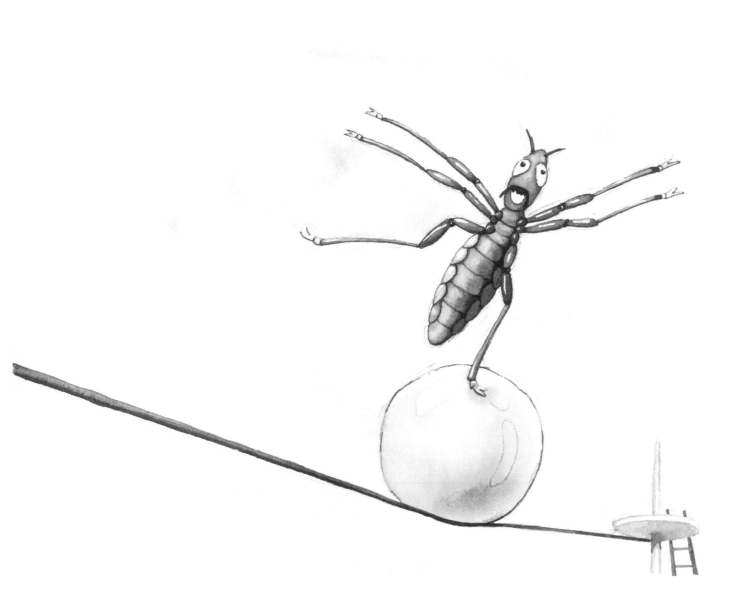

Goodnight

Goodnight Mummy, goodnight Daddy,
Goodnight Granny and Grandad.
Goodnight doggy, goodnight pusscat,
Goodnight TV and table lamp.
Goodnight sofa, goodnight chair,
Goodnight cupboard under the stair.
Some people they count sheep,
But I just say "Goodnight".
It helps me to fall asleep,
Now please turn out the li...

Quick Quiz

1) How many sheep are there in "Goodnight"?
2) What does Asparagus Pickle think goes well with bogies?
3) What does Barnaby Flea balance on?
4) What colour are Jelly Dog's wellies?
5) In "Best Friend" what is the name of the dog that goes to school?
6) What day is football played in "Busy Bee"?
7) What is the ice cream van's number plate in "99 Please"?
8) What gets caught in "Fishing"?
9) How many different types of animal are there in this book?
10) Can you actually stand on custard?

Good luck!

You can download 'Standing on Custard' to your iPad or iPhone from the iBooks Store.

Also by Jo Burke:

A Squirrel's Tail
Molly, Chip and the Chair

For more information about Jo's books or to order online go to:
www.standingoncustard.com